The New Pet

What will the new pet be?

G000114313

Walkthrough

...w Pet'.

...m.

Look at the picture.

What has the little girl got ready for her pet?

What do you think the new pet could be?

Walkthrough

This is the back cover – let's read the blurb together.

'What will the new pet be?'

(Prompt for suggestions.)

Walkthrough

This is the title page.

Let's read the title again.

What do you think is in the box?

What sort of pet might be in it?

Read the names of the author, illustrator and publisher.

Walkthrough

Who is in the picture? (*a girl*)

What is she doing? (*thinking*)

How do you know she is thinking? (*gesture and expression*)

 Observe and Prompt

Word Recognition

- Check the children can read 'a'. (This is a sight word.)

- Check the children can read the word 'girl'. (This is a sight word – a word that is likely to be in their store of familiar words.) However, if they struggle, tell them the initial letter and sound and model the blending of this word for them.

- If the children have difficulty with the word 'basket', ask them if they recognise the initial letter and sound – 'b'. Then ask them if they can try to blend the sounds, from left to right, through the word.

a girl

2

Walkthrough

What is this?

What is it for?

a basket

3

 **Observe and Prompt**

Language Comprehension

- What do the children think the girl is thinking about?

- What do the children think the basket might be for?

- Check the children read with left-to-right directionality.

Walkthrough

What is the little girl holding?

(Children may suggest 'blanket'. Tell them it is a 'rug' which is like a blanket).

 Observe and Prompt

Word Recognition

- Check the children are reading 'rug' using their decoding skills. Can they sound out and blend r-u-g all through the word?

- If the children have difficulty with the word 'bowl', ask them if they recognise the initial letter and sound – 'b'. Then tell them this word and model the reading of it for them.

a rug

4

Walkthrough

What is the little girl looking at?

What kind of pet uses a bowl?

a bowl

5

 Observe and Prompt

Language Comprehension

- Ask the children what else the girl has seen.
- Ask the children what these items might be used for. Can they predict what is going to happen?

Walkthrough

What is happening in the picture now?

How do you think the little girl is feeling?
(*excited*)

How do you know? (*little girl is on tiptoes*)

How would you feel?

👁 Observe and Prompt

Word Recognition

- Check the children are reading 'box' using their decoding skills. Can they sound out and blend b-o-x all through the word?

- If the children have difficulty with the word 'nose', ask them if they recognise the initial letter and sound – 'n'. Model the reading of this word for them.

a box

6

6

Walkthrough

Which bit of the pet can you see?
Emphasise 'a nose'.

What will happen next?

a nose

7

Language Comprehension

- Ask the children what is happening now in the story.

- How do the children think the girl is feeling?

- Ask the children to predict what will happen next in the story.

Walkthrough

What is the new pet?

Do you think the puppy likes the little girl?

How do you know?

How does the little girl feel?

a puppy

8

 Observe and Prompt

Word Recognition

- Check the children can read 'puppy'. If they have difficulty, prompt them to blend the sounds through the word, from left to right. Explain the 'y' at the end makes the 'ee' sound.

 Observe and Prompt

Language Comprehension

- Ask the children what has happened at the end of the story.

- How do the children think the girl feels? How would they feel?